World War II
Trivia Quiz Book

ANSWERS TO YOUR
QUESTIONS ABOUT
WORLD WAR II

World War II Trivia Quiz Book

ANSWERS TO YOUR QUESTIONS ABOUT WORLD WAR II

Gerard & Patricia Del Re

BARNES
&NOBLE
BOOKS
NEW YORK

The authors would like to give special thanks to Josephine Velez for her counsel and historic scholarship.

2001 Barnes & Noble Books

ISBN 0-7607-2605-1

Text design by Lundquist Design, New York

Printed and bound in the United States of America

01 02 03 MP 9 8 7 6 5 5 4 3 2

OPM

Q: Name the major countries that formed the Allied forces.

Q: Name the major countries that formed the Axis powers.

Q: What WWII dictator was once imprisoned for opposing war?

Q: What dictator was once tried for treason and sentenced to five years in prison?

Q: What dictator of the Axis powers was once a journalist?

A: Great Britain, France, the Soviet Union, and the United States were the four largest powers in the Allied forces. Other countries contributing included China, Australia, Canada, and other British Commonwealth countries.

A: The major countries that formed the Axis powers were Germany, Italy, and Japan. Other allies of the Axis powers included Finland, Slovakia, Hungary, Croatia, Romania, and Bulgaria.

A: Benito Mussolini was imprisoned for opposing Italy's war in Libya (1911–1912).

A: Adolph Hitler. On November 8, 1923 Hitler led an uprising in Munich (known as the Beer Hall Putsch) hoping to ignite a general revolt, but failed. The army crushed the uprising, Hitler was arrested, tried, and found guilty of treason and sentenced to five years in prison. Within less than a year, however, he was released.

A: Benito Mussolini, dictator and the father of Italian Fascism, was a journalist before he became Italy's leader. He was editor of a newspaper entitled *Avanti*, the socialist party newspaper in Milan. After he was expelled from the party, he started his own newspaper, *Il Popola d'Italia* (The People of Italy).

Q: What is *Mein Kampf*?

Q: What was the original title of *Mein Kampf*?

Q: Who did Mussolini use as scapegoats for Italy's problems?

Q: Who did Hitler blame for Germany's problems?

Q: What did all of Hitler's SS (*Schutzstaffeln*) personnel have in common regarding appearance?

Q: Who was *Time* magazine's Man of the Year in 1938?

Q: What was Hitler's profession before becoming a dictator?

A: *Mein Kampf* (My Struggle) is a two-volume book written by Hitler, the first volume completed while he was in prison (1925) and the second after his release in 1926. In it he claimed that the Germans belonged to a superior "Aryan" race that was destined to control all of the inferior races, as well as the world.

A: In 1924 Adolf Hitler, imprisoned in Germany, dictated to Rudolf Hess a book entitled *Four and a Half Years of Struggle Against Lies, Stupidity and Cowardice; Settling Accounts with the Destroyers of the National Socialist Movement.* That title was changed to *Mein Kampf.*

A: Mussolini blamed Italy's problems on foreigners.

A: Hitler blamed Germany's problems on foreign powers, communists, and Jews, who he claimed controlled world's finances.

A: The SS, who were the black-shirted Nazi Party elite corps, were all without facial hair. Only Hitler was allowed his famous "moustachelet," as it was called.

A: Adolf Hitler.

A: Before becoming dictator of Germany, Hitler was an unsuccessful artist and an infantry soldier during WWI. He was decorated with the Iron Cross First and Second Class.

Q: Who said: "Whoever wants to understand the National Socialist German Workers Party (Nazis) must know Wagner"?

Q: Was Adolf Hitler born in Germany?

Q: What was the Third Reich?

Q: What did Adolf Hitler say about the longevity of the Third Reich?

Q: Where did the term "Nazi" originate?

Q: Who, on September 30, 1938, waved a piece of paper that claimed to guarantee "peace for our time"?

A: Adolf Hitler.

A: No. Hitler was born in Braunau, Austria on April 20, 1889.

A: The Nazis believed that their rule was successor to the Holy Roman Empire and the German Empire. They called their regime the Third Reich.

A: He boasted that the Third Reich's reign would last a thousand years.

A: Nazi was the short, and originally derisive, term for the *Nationalsozialistische Deutsche Arbeiterpartei*, or *NSDAP* (National Socialist German Worker's Party). The original abbreviation was *NASOS*.

A: Neville Chamberlain, Prime Minister of England. In front of 10 Downing Street, Chamberlain held up a piece of paper with Hitler's signature, which allowed Hitler to grab the Sudetenland (the German-speaking part of Czechoslovakia) in return for that nation's freedom. Within six months Hitler broke his promise with the invasion of Prague, Czechoslovakia's capital.

Q: What was *Kristallnacht*?

Q: What did the Nazis claim was the cause of *Kristallnacht*?

Q: What were the casualties of *Kristallnacht*?

Q: Who signed a nonaggression pact on August 23, 1939?

A: *Kristallnacht*, or the "Night of Broken Glass," was a massive attack that targeted Jews, which began on the night of November 9, 1938 and lasted well into the next day. All over Germany, Austria, and other Nazi controlled areas, the windows of Jewish shops, homes and synagogues were broken and all contents that lay beyond the glass were destroyed.

A: To avenge the mistreatment of his family, a 17-year-old Jewish boy named Herschel Grynszpan assassinated Third Secretary Ernst von Rath, a German official in Paris. The Germans then ordered the attacks on the Jews that came to be known as *Kristallnacht*.

A: It was estimated that during *Kristallnacht* 7,500 Jewish businesses were destroyed, 1,000 synagogues were burnt, about 96 Jewish people died, and 30,000 were sent to concentration camps.

A: Adolf Hitler of Germany and Joseph Stalin of the Soviet Union secretly agreed to divide Eastern Europe between themselves. Hitler eventually betrayed Stalin; on June 22, 1941 the Nazis fanned out in three directions and invaded the Soviet Union—one column of troops headed for Moscow, another for Leningrad and a third for the Ukraine. Hitler's betrayal caused Stalin to have a nervous breakdown.

Q: What secret ambition did both Hitler and Stalin share?

Q: Which leader, Winston Churchill or Adolf Hitler, had the better understanding of the United States' ability to become a strong military force in WWII?

Q: What does *Führer* mean?

Q: Why did Britain and France declare war on Germany on September 3, 1939, beginning WWII?

Q: What was a U-Boat?

Q: What was the Gestapo?

A: At one time in their lives, Adolf Hitler and Joseph Stalin both wanted to become priests. During one of his family moves, Hitler lived for six months across from a Benedictine monastery; it was then he dreamt of entering the priesthood. Joseph Stalin briefly studied to become a priest until 1903, when he joined the revolutionaries.

A: Churchill. Before the war began in 1939, Churchill had visited the U.S. and understood how vast and rich in resources the country was. Hitler rarely left Germany.

A: *Führer* means leader, or great leader, in German. Hitler adopted the title when he combined the offices of president and chancellor and took over the German empire.

A: The German invasion of Poland on September 1, 1939 was a contributing factor in the declaration, as was the sinking of the Cunard passenger vessel *Athenia* off the Irish Coast, killing 112 people, also on September 1, 1939.

A: A U-Boat was a submarine, from the German *unterseeboot*, or underwater boat.

A: The Gestapo was the German secret police that Hermann Goering founded in April, 1933. Their sole purpose was the persecution of all political opponents of the Nazi party. Their job was proactive as well as reactive. Those who were arrested by the Gestapo were usually placed in concentration camps.

Q: What was the Pact of Steel?

Q: What was the Tripartite Pact?

Q: What was the Maginot Line?

Q: What does *blitzkrieg* mean?

Q: What was the *blitzkrieg*?

A: The Pact of Steel was a military pact signed by Germany and Italy on May 22, 1939.

A: The Tripartite Pact, signed in Berlin on September 27, 1940, bound Germany, Japan, and Italy as comrades-in-arms. According to the Pact, Italy and Germany recognized Japan's intention to "create a new order in all the Asiatic space," and, in turn, Japan recognized the right of Germany and Italy to "create a new European order."

A: The Maginot Line (named after War Minister Andre Maginot) was the French system of fortifications that stretched along the 200-mile Franco-German frontier and ran from Thionville to Belfort; the French considered it impregnable. The Germans advanced from Belgium, sweeping around the line in 1940 in swiftly moving armored columns. The Maginot Line was built during the 1930s.

A: *Blitzkrieg* means lightning war in German.

A: The *blitzkrieg* was a military tactic, employing rapidly-moving military forces, designed to create psychological shock and disorganization among the enemy. This tactic of using surprise, speed, and superior armaments was employed successfully by the Germans against Poland, Belgium, France, and the Netherlands.

Q: When did France surrender to Germany?

Q: What was "the Miracle at Dunkirk"?

Q: What was the *Luftwaffe*?

Q: In the summer of 1940, the *Luftwaffe* was a mighty weapon, yet was not very successful against the outnumbered British air service. Why?

Q: What do the initials RAF stand for?

Q: What made the British Spitfire fighter planes so valuable in the Battle of Britain?

A: On June 22, 1940 France surrendered to Germany, and three days later the armistice was signed, giving Germany control of northern France and the Atlantic coast.

A: Between May 26 and June 4, 1940, the British were able to evacuate 330,000 British and French troops from the French port of Dunkirk.

A: The *Luftwaffe* was the German air force.

A: With the newly invented radar to warn the British of oncoming German bombers, and with ample fuel because the British were not flying great distances, they were able to mount a strong defense in what became known as the Battle of Britain.

A: RAF is an acronym for Royal Air Force.

A: During the Battle of Britain, nothing the *Luftwaffe* had could top the speed and maneuverability of the British-built Supermarine Spitfire. Designed by R. J. Mitchell, the Spitfire was a low-wing single-seat monoplane that was one of the fastest and most effective planes in the air; it had a top speed of 360 miles per hour, and had the ability to climb at 2,500 feet per minute.

Q: Who were "the few," according to Winston Churchill?

Q: What was the most important technological advance in the area of aerial surveillance created in WWII?

Q: What was the U.S. Lend-Lease program?

Q: What law passed on October 9, 1940 would affect young people across America?

A: The term "the few" applies to the RAF pilots who fought in the Battle of Britain against the Germans. Winston Churchill said of the great air battle won by the British, "Never in the field of human conflict was so much owed by so many to so few."

A: Radar (an acronym for Radio Detection And Ranging) was invented in 1932. Radar was first used in WWII, greatly contributing to many battles like the Battle of Britain. Radar allowed both sides to know the locations of enemy aircraft before they could actually see them.

A: The Lend-Lease Bill, approved by the U.S. Congress on March 11, 1941, was the ingenious idea of President Roosevelt, and allowed the U.S. to loan arms to countries fighting the Axis powers. The U.S. could aid "any country whose defense the President deems vital to the defense of the United States." The United States gave Lend-Lease aid to over thirty nations.

A: The establishment of the first peacetime military draft in the U.S. Young men 18 years and older would be obliged to report to their local draft boards for military service.

Q: What was the Atlantic Charter?

Q: Can you name the only Middle Eastern country to sign a pact with Nazi Germany?

Q: When did the Japanese bombing of Pearl Harbor take place?

Q: What were the names of the admiral and the lieutenant general relieved of their commands in the aftermath of the attack on Pearl Harbor?

Q: What was the name of the admiral who was put in charge of the U.S. Pacific fleet after Pearl Harbor?

A: The Atlantic Charter was an agreement between U.S. President Roosevelt and British Prime Minister Churchill, concerning human rights and war goals. Roosevelt and Churchill met aboard a ship off the coast of Newfoundland on August 9, 1941.

A: Turkey, on June 8, 1941. The Allies desperately entreated Turkey not to do so, but to no avail.

A: On December 7, 1941, at 7:55 A.M., the Japanese bombed Pearl Harbor, located on the island of Oahu. The attack, which was the climax to a decade of tension between the United States and Japan, killed 2,323 U.S. servicemen. In addition, eight battleships, three destroyers, and three cruises were put out of action, and two battleships, the *Oklahoma* and *Arizona*, were completely destroyed.

A: Admiral H. E. Kimmel and Lieutenant General Walter C. Short were both blamed by the Navy's top brass for being unprepared at Pearl Harbor.

A: Admiral Chester N. Nimitz was given command of the Pacific Fleet on December 17, 1941, appointed by Navy Secretary Frank Knox. Nimitz's great leadership and tactical skills helped lead the Allies to victory.

Q: When did the U.S. declare war on Japan?

Q: When did Germany declare war on the U.S.?

Q: Why did Japan not conquer or attempt to conquer Australia, a country not far from Japan?

Q: What leader of the Axis powers was thought by his people to be a descendent of a god?

Q: What was the year of Bob Hope's first performance for the troops?

Q: Who were the Fifth Columnists?

A: On December 8, 1941, the day after the horrific bombing of Pearl Harbor, President Roosevelt addressed the U.S. Congress saying that December 7 is "a date that will live in infamy." After a vote of 82–0 in the U.S. Senate and 388–1 in the House in favor of declaring war on Japan, Roosevelt signed the official declaration of war.

A: On December 11, 1941, Germany and Italy declared war on the United States, forcing President Roosevelt to put an end to official U.S. neutrality in Europe. The U.S. at that point was formally at war with the powerful Axis Powers.

A: Perhaps the Japanese had hoped to do so, but when American and Australian forces invaded New Guinea, which was occupied by Japan, an invasion of Australia by Japan was out of the question.

A: Emperor Hirohito of Japan was thought to be a descendent of the Shinto Goddess Amaterasu, and therefore considered divine.

A: May 6, 1941 at March Field, California.

A: Fifth Columnists were Nazi secret agents and sympathizers who created unrest behind enemy lines by committing acts of sabotage.

Q: What Italian monastery bombed by the Allies became a German stronghold?

Q: What humanitarian organization owned and operated an ammunition factory during WWII and beyond?

Q: What did the Drury Lane Theatre donate to the British military during WWII?

Q: Who invented K-Rations?

Q: What was Operation Barbarossa?

A: The Benedictine Abbey on Monte Cassino, 1702 feet above the main road between Rome to Naples. Thousands died at the Battle of Mounte Cassino before it fell to Polish forces in May 1944. The abbey was rebuilt and commemorated by Pope Paul VI in 1965.

A: The Finnish chapter of the Red Cross found itself the owner of Oy Sako Ad Army Factory. Oy Sako Ad donated the factory to the Red Cross when it was feared that the Soviet Union might confiscate it when it occupied Finland. Unable to reconcile its dual roles as lifesaver and arms manufacturer, the Red Cross relinquished the firm in 1962.

A: Arms. The famed London theater, having heard the British were short of firearms, contributed its prop store of twelve rusty rifles in an arrangement through the London Home Guard. The Drury Lane Theatre remains the only legitimate theater to have ventured into the arms business in the name of patriotism.

A: Ancel Keys, a professor at the University of Minnesota. K-Rations were food for U.S. WWII troops, packed in three-ounce tins. The rations included beef, pork, chocolate, and crackers, among other things.

A: It was the planned German invasion of the Soviet Union, which began on June 22, 1941.

Q: How did Operation Barbarossa obtain its name?

Q: Whose name meant "man of steel"?

Q: Why was DDT widely used as an offensive weapon in the South Pacific during WWII?

Q: What was the Hollywood Canteen?

Q: What was the relationship between Douglas MacArthur, Winston Churchill, and Franklin Delano Roosevelt?

A: Hitler changed the name of the invasion of Russia from Operation Fritz to Operation Barbarossa in honor of Fredrick Barbarossa, the Holy Roman Emperor who had wanted to conquer the Holy Land in 1190.

A: Joseph Stalin, born Joseph Vissarionovich Djugashvili in 1879. By 1913, he was using the pseudonym of Stalin, which means "man of steel" in Russian.

A: DDT was used on plants and brush in the South Pacific to destroy insects, thereby reducing the risk of such illnesses as malaria and typhus.

A: The Hollywood Canteen, opened on October 17, 1942, was co-founded by Bette Davis and John Garfield, with generous financial support from the film studios, as a place of hospitality for members of the Armed Forces. It was designed to help cheer up lonely servicemen, providing entertainment and meals. Film stars mixed with servicemen, giving autographs and putting on skits. The Hollywood Canteen closed on November 22, 1945.

A: U.S. General Douglas MacArthur was the eighth cousin of British Prime Minister Winston Churchill and the sixth cousin of U.S. President Franklin D. Roosevelt. The common ancestor that this trio of leaders shared was Sarah Barney Belcher of Tauton, Massachusetts.

Q: Did General MacArthur believe in engaging in battles which resulted in victories over all Japanese military units, down to the last man?

Q: Where did the Allies mistakenly bomb on November 4, 1943?

Q: Who was Private Chips?

Q: Who made the statement "A single death is a tragedy, a million deaths is a statistic"?

Q: Who was secretary of war during the Roosevelt WWII years (1941–1945)?

Q: When did the secretary of war cease to be a member of the president's cabinet?

A: No! Since Japanese forces were often entrenched on small Pacific islands, General MacArthur felt that it was unnecessary to conquer every island on his march toward Japan.

A: The Vatican. A formal letter of apology was hand delivered to Pope Pious XII.

A: U.S. Private Chips was a German Shepherd-Collie mix whose exploits during WWII gained him the Purple Heart, the Silver Star, and the Distinguished Service Medal in a ceremony on November 19, 1943. Chips risked his life on numerous occasions, including routing Italian soldiers from their lethal machinegun nest, saving many GIs lives. No dog in the history of the U.S. military has ever been so honored.

A: Joseph Stalin. The Soviet dictator lived up to that statement by sending millions of political prisoners to the Gulag, where many died from starvation and exposure.

A: During the Roosevelt war years the secretary of war was Henry L. Stanton, who replaced Henry H. Woodring (1936–1940).

A: The secretary of war ceased to be a member of the president's cabinet with the creation of the Department of Defense in 1947.

Q: Why was sugar rationed during WWII?

Q: What was the only U.S. state that did not have a battleship named after it?

Q: What building was designed to house the increasing number of WWII administrators?

Q: What was Code Mammoth?

Q: Can you name the only U.S. general who would go on to win a Nobel Prize after WWII?

A: Sugar was rationed because of possible shortages. Sugar was used in the production of alcohol, which is an ingredient in explosives. Most of our sugar was imported from the Philippines, West Indies, and Hawaii.

A: Montana.

A: The Pentagon, completed on January 15, 1943 in Arlington, Virginia, was built at a cost of 83 million dollars, and touted as the worlds largest building. It consisted of 65 million square feet of floor space, 17 miles of corridors, and had 7,748 windows.

A: Code Mammoth (*Mammut*) was the name of the German project to develop a super-heavy tank. The first prototype was the *Maus* (Mouse), which was designed by Ferdinand Porsche and built by Krupp. It weighed 180 tons, was 30 feet long, and had 10 inches of impenetrable steel plating. It moved at a snail's pace, and when rolling upon soft earth, the tank sank as if in quicksand. Seeing them as impractical, Hitler ordered that all work cease, and had the prototypes destroyed, rather than risk them falling into Allied hands.

A: General George Marshall was awarded the Noble Prize in 1953 for his work rebuilding war-torn Europe (the Marshall Plan).

Q: What was unusual about the activation of the U.S. 99th Fighter Squadron, "the Tuskegee," on March 22, 1941?

Q: How many decorations were awarded to the Tuskegee?

Q: Why was the song "Dear Friend" by Rodgers and Hammerstein significant to WWII?

Q: What was Heinrich Himmler's occupation prior to becoming head of the Nazi SS?

Q: What did beer, whiskey, and meat have to do with Adolf Hitler's diet?

Q: What went on display December 2, 1942 at the New York Public Library?

A: The 99th Squadron was the first all African-American fighter squadron activated by the U.S. Congress. They got the name Tuskegee from the army airfield—located in Tuskegee, Alabama—where the training for all the African-American fighter pilots during WWII took place.

A: They won over 850 medals, including 150 Distinguished Flying Crosses, 8 Purple Hearts, 14 Bronze Stars, 744 Air Medals, and 3 Unit Citations. They flew over 15, 233 sorties between May 1943 and June 9, 1945.

A: William Music published the song on July 13, 1944, and donated all proceeds from the sale of the sheet music and recordings to the WWII Relief Funds 5th War Loan Drive.

A: He was a chicken farmer.

A: Nothing—the Führer neither drank alcoholic beverages nor ate meat.

A: An exhibit entitled "Books Banned by the Nazis." Books by H. G. Wells, John Steinbeck, Theodore Dreiser, Thomas Hardy, and others were deemed not pure enough for the Nazis.

Q: What did Betty Grable auction off at a WWII War Bond rally for $40,000?

Q: What part of women's clothing was recycled to make parachutes during WWII?

Q: What was the only movie *musical* with a WWII background that won an Oscar for Best Picture?

Q: Names the films with WWII backgrounds, or about WWII, that won Oscars for best picture.

Q: Who designed the insignia on P.T. boats depicting a mosquito astride a torpedo?

Q: What was the only comic book Mussolini did not ban during WWII?

Q: Who was Adolf Hitler's architect and munitions chief?

A: A pair of her nylon stockings.

A: Nylons.

A: *The Sound of Music* (1965).

A: *Mrs. Miniver*, staring Greer Garson (1942); *The Best Years of Our Lives*, starring Fredric March (1946); *From Here to Eternity*, starring Burt Lancaster, Frank Sinatra, Montgomery Clift (1953); *The Bridge on the River Kwai*, starring Alec Guinness (1957); *The Sound of Music*, starring Julie Andrews (1965); *Patton*, starring George C. Scott (1970); *Schindler's List*, starring Liam Neeson (1993).

A: Walt Disney.

A: Mickey Mouse comic books. Mussolini loved Mickey Mouse almost as much as Walt Disney.

A: Albert Speer.

Q: What WWII-era medical distinction can Peoria, Illinois claim?

Q: How did the United States treat Japanese-Americans during WWII?

Q: How many internment camps were set up in the United States?

Q: What was the Tule Lake riot?

A: Penicillin was developed at the U.S. Department of Agriculture Laboratory at Peoria, IL. The medicine proved invaluable against bacterial infection of wounds.

A: Due to an enormous amount of pressure placed upon President Roosevelt, he signed papers forcing those of Japanese blood who lived in the United States to be placed in internment camps (also known as Japanese relocation camps) during WWII. This forced Japanese-Americans to leave their homes and jobs and move into these camps.

A: Ten internment camps were set up in Arkansas, California, Idaho, Utah, Arizona, Wyoming, and Colorado. An estimated 120,000 people of Japanese ancestry were placed in camps between 1941 until 1945.

A: Tule Lake was one of the internment camps located in California, where a riot occurred on November 4, 1943. Martial law was declared, and the military police put an end to the riot.

Q: Why did President Truman say to the 442nd Regimental Combat Team "You fought not only the enemy, but you fought prejudice—and you have won"?

Q: What battalion during WWII was nicknamed the Purple Heart Battalion?

Q: What did the Soviet Red Army train dogs to do to tanks during WWII?

Q: What was the importance of Lt. Colonel James H. "Jimmy" Doolittle's celebrated daytime bombing attack on Tokyo on April 18, 1942?

A: The 442ⁿᵈ was an all-Japanse-American battalion that won numerous decorations for their heroic deeds against Italy and Germany. The battalion was awarded in excess of 18,000 decorations, including 7 Presidential Citations, 52 Distinguished Service Crosses, 1 Distinguished Service Medal, 560 Silver Stars (28 with Oak-leaf Clusters), 4,000 Bronze Stars, 22 Legions of Merit, 12 *Croix de Guerre*, and 9,486 Purple Hearts.

A: The 442nd Regimental Combat Team had suffered so many injuries and deaths at Monte Cassino that it was nicknamed the Purple Heart Battalion.

A: They trained dogs to destroy enemy tanks. With explosive devices strapped to their backs, the dogs would crawl beneath a tank, where they had been trained to expect food. The friction between the belly of the tank and the device would detonate the explosives, destroying the tank (and the dog). The plan did not always work; since the dogs were trained using Soviet tanks they sometimes chose them over the enemy's. Despite this, however, about twenty-five German tanks were put out of action using this unconventional method during the battles for Stalingrad and Kursk.

A: The Doolittle raid, with sixteen B-25 Mitchell bombers, was a daring strike at the heart of Japan. While the raid did not accomplish much militarily, it damaged the confidence of the Japanese, and was a tremendous boost to American morale, which had suffered during the months of losses.

Q: Who were the "Night Witches"?

Q: How many missions were credited to the Night Witches?

Q: What did the "B" in B-17 and B-29 stand for?

Q: How were the belly-gunners of the B-17's usually chosen?

Q: What were the heavy bomber fighter planes the U.S. used in WWII?

Q: What was "*Tora Tora Tora*"?

A: They were the thousands of Soviet women who served with the *Voyenno–Vozdushniya* (the Soviet airforces). In 1942, one of the three air regiments that were formed of female volunteers was the 588th Women's Night Bomber Regiment, called *Nachthexen* by the Germans, or the "Night Witches." They flew Polikarpov Po-2 biplanes. Thousands won orders and medals.

A: The Night Witches flew more than 24,000 sorties and dropped about 23,000 tons of bombs.

A: Bomber.

A: The belly-gunners of the B-17 were usually chosen based on height: the man *lacking* height would have the "honor" of becoming the gunner.

A: The Boeing B-17 Flying Fortress, the B-24 Liberator, B-25 Mitchell, and the B-29 Super Fortress.

A: *Tora Tora Tora* (tiger tiger tiger in Japanese) was a code used by the Japanese during WWII that meant "We have succeeded in the surprise attack."

Q: When General Douglas MacArthur made his famous vow "I shall return" in 1942, where was he promising to return to?

Q: What language was used as a code by the marines during WWII?

Q: What German manufactured items owned by citizens of Great Britain did the British government request be donated or sold to aid in the war effort?

Q: What peculiar distinction did Army Privates C. H. Kuhl and P. G. Bennet share in WWII?

A: The Philippine Islands—he had been forced off the islands by the Japanese in 1942. In 1944 MacArthur did return to the Philippines to defeat the Japanese and gain forever after the gratitude of the Philippine people.

A: The need for an unbreakable code arose during WWII, as the enemies were intercepting and deciphering important messages. Phillip Johnston, who had lived among the Navaho for over twenty years, suggested to Major General Clayton that the military use the Navaho language—an unwritten language unknown to anyone but the Navaho—as a code. After a demonstration, this brainstorm of one man helped to create an unbreakable code for the marines.

A: During WWII, the British government pleaded with their citizens to donate or sell their Leica and Contax cameras to the British government. The simple reason for this was that, at the time, the Germans made the best cameras—and the government needed the best.

A: Both were slapped by General George S. Patton for displaying emotional behavior. C. H. Kuhl was slapped across the face by Patton on August 3, 1943; Bennet on August 10, 1943. The press had a field day at Patton's expense. His superior, General Eisenhower, admonished Patton for his crude and unprofessional conduct.

Q: What famous commander of the Axis powers was forced to commit suicide?

Q: Which Japanese fighter pilot did America dub "the Devil"?

Q: Who was Collette Nirouet?

Q: Who was the only woman awarded both the German Iron Cross and the *Luftwaffe* Diamond Clasp?

Q: What division of the American military had the largest fleet during WWII?

A: General Erwin Rommel, commander of the German Armies, was suspected of conspiring to assassinate Adolf Hitler (July 20, 1944). Because of this he was given two options. His first option was to stand trial for his supposed deeds, leaving his family's lives at risk. Rommel's second choice was suicide; if he committed suicide he would receive a hero's burial and, most importantly, his family would be left unharmed. Rommel chose suicide, and on October 4, 1944 he ended his life by taking cyanide.

A: Hiroyoshi Nishizawa was Japan's ace fighter pilot of the Mitsubishi A6M Zero. He was never bested in a battle, but died on a cargo plane that was shot down by American soldiers on October 26, 1944.

A: She was a teenaged girl who disguised herself as a man in order to join the French Army. She died in action, and was awarded posthumously a *Croix de Guerre*.

A: Hanna Rietch. She was a civilian who tested military aircraft, and piloted members of the German high command throughout the war.

A: Contrary to popular belief, the U.S. Army had a larger fleet than the U.S. Navy—111,000 ships as opposed to 75,000. However, the army's fleet consisted mainly of support and transport vessels.

Q: Which president served as a U.S. Navy fighter-pilot in WWII?

Q: Who were the eight future U.S. presidents on active or inactive duty during WWII?

Q: Was the *Waffen* SS comprised only of Germans?

Q: What was the only country that Germany declared war on in WWII?

A: George H. W. Bush. After becoming, at nineteen, the youngest navy fighter-pilot, Bush flew fifty-eight WWII missions.

A: Dwight D. Eisenhower, Allied Supreme Commander; John F. Kennedy, a junior officer and hero in the navy; Lyndon B. Johnson, a staff officer (he was ordered back to Congress before he saw battle); Richard M. Nixon, a junior officer in the navy in the Pacific; Gerald R. Ford, a naval officer who served on a carrier; James E. Carter, a student at the U.S. Naval Academy (the only future president who was on inactive duty during WWII); Ronald Reagan, a captain in the army (he made training films in Hollywood because his eyesight was poor); and George Bush (he flew with the Avengers, was shot down and wounded, and was awarded the Distinguished Flying Cross).

A: No. The *Waffen* SS divisions, who were the elite combat troops, had over one-half million non-German members, including Bosnians, Croatians, Soviet prisoners, Dutch, and Ukrainians.

A: On December 11, 1941, Germany declared war on the United States of America. Germany did not have official declarations of war with all the other countries with which it was at war.

Q: What WWII general was granted the title of Master of Sword?

Q: Can you name the only WWII conscientious objector to be awarded the Congressional Medal of Honor?

Q: Who was Japan's prime minister during WWII?

Q: What was the Rape of Nanking?

A: General Patton was the only American to be granted the title of Master of Sword at the French Army Cavalry School at Saumur.

A: U.S. Army Private First Class Desmond Doss, who refused to fight or carry a weapon because of religious beliefs, and was assigned to the medical corps. Doss risked his life numerous times in order to minister to the wounded and dying. On one occasion he carried fifty men, one at a time, to the edge of a cliff and lowered each by rope to safety. Twice wounded, he moved bravely through machine gun fire to bring medical care. On October 12, 1945, the Seventh Day Adventist was awarded the Medal of Honor by President Harry S. Truman.

A: In 1941, after Kinoye Fumimaro's resignation, Hideki Tojo became Prime Minister of Japan. Tojo was the one who approved the attack on Pearl Harbor; he also pushed the Japanese offensive in the Pacific and Asia. He resigned in July 1944 after he lost Saipan in the Marianas. Before his arrest in 1945, he tried to commit suicide but failed; he was then tried and hanged by the Allied powers.

A: During the Sino-Japanese War that preceded World War II, the Japanese Imperial Army massacred over 100,000 citizens when it seized Nanking, China, on December 13, 1937. In the six weeks that followed, the Japanese army carried out mass executions, thousands of rapes, and destroyed more than a third of the city's buildings.

Q: What unusual fact concerning Charles Lindbergh was released only after the end of WWII?

Q: How close to the United States did the German military come during WWII?

Q: What was the WASP?

Q: What kind of training did WASPs receive?

A: In 1944 Charles Lindbergh, while flying a P-38 in his capacity as advisor and trainer of U.S. pilots, encountered a Japanese fighter plane. Lucky Lindy's plane was equipped with gunnery, so when the Japanese fighter crossed his flight path, Lindbergh fired his guns, sending the enemy plane descending in a trail of smoke and fire into the Pacific. The Lindbergh incident was kept confidential until after the war because of Lindbergh's civilian status.

A: The German submarine service operated in waters just offshore along the east coast of the United States. The Germans fired on and sank several merchant ships departing from American ports with supply cargoes for the European Allies.

A: WASPs (Women's Airforce Service Pilots) were the first women in history trained to fly American military aircraft. The mother of the WASP was Jacqueline Cochran, an accomplished woman pilot who had served as a ferry pilot for the RAF. Over one thousand women pilots had enlisted during WWII, ferrying all sorts of aircraft during WWII.

A: All WASP trainees had to endure the same primary, basic, and advanced training that their male counterparts did. Upon completion of their training—or earning their wings—the WASPs went to special training to learn how to pilot such planes as the B-17s and B-26s.

Q: What was the WAAC?

Q: What were the duties of the WACs?

Q: What were the WAVES?

Q: What was "the enigma"?

A: The WAAC (Women's Army Auxiliary Corps) was the creation of Congresswoman Edith Nourse Rogers (1941). WAAC was created to work with the army and allowed women to receive food, uniforms and pay. Women were not allowed to command men. Over 140,000 women served in WAAC during WWII. WAAC was later changed to WAC (Women's Army Corps).

A: The WACs served in many different positions throughout the war, working as truck drivers, aviation mechanics, and hospital orderlies. They issued weapons, worked in laboratories, and tested field equipment.

A: The WAVES (Women Accepted for Volunteer Emergency Service) was a women's auxiliary service of the U.S. Navy which operated in much the same way as WAC.

A: The enigma was a German typewriter-like coding machine used throughout WWII. Its advantage was that intercepted messages could not be deciphered except with a duplicate of the machine. Luckily, the British were able to reconstruct it, allowing them to read German secret transmissions.

Q: How did the Germans lose the chance to capture Moscow?

Q: What was the outcome of the Battle of Stalingrad (August 1942–February 1943)?

Q: What was significant about the naval Battle of Midway?

Q: What was the Island Hopping Campaign?

Q: Who said: "Among the Americans serving on Iwo island, uncommon valor was a common virtue"?

A: Neither the Germans nor their machines were outfitted to handle the extreme cold of the Russian winters. In December 1941, the German generals commanding the armies reported that they were stopped, their tanks freezing, and the troops losing their will to fight. The Germans, who had reached the suburbs of the capital, had to halt their offensive.

A: The Battle of Stalingrad ended with a decisive Soviet victory that stopped the German Sixth Army advance; it was the beginning of the end for the Germans on the Eastern front. Over one million Soviet soldiers and over 800,000 German soldiers died in the Stalingrad campaign.

A: The Battle of Midway (June 3–6, 1942) was a decisive naval engagement that established the United States sea power over the Japanese. The victory successfully terminated a major Japanese attempt to capture the Midway Islands (northwest of Honolulu).

A: One of the war strategies used by the U.S. in the Pacific War. The marines would assault one island after another; the air-fields captured were used to launch new attacks on successive islands. In this way they moved closer and closer to the Japanese mainland.

A: Admiral Chester A. Nimitz, in reference to the soldiers fighting the Battle of Iwo Jima, the bloodiest battle in the history of the Marine Corps. The Battle of Iwo Jima yielded one-fourth of the Medals of Honor given in the war.

Q: How long did the battle at Guadalcanal last?

Q: What role did Fleet Admiral Ernest King play in WWII?

Q: What were the *kamikazes*?

Q: When did the first *kamikaze* attack occur?

Q: What were the *shinyo*?

A: The battle at Guadalcanal lasted five months and resulted in the evacuation by the Japanese in ships. The U.S. Marines landed on Guadalcanal on August 7, 1942 and battled the Japanese in this tropical climate from August 24 to November 30, while the navy fought six major engagements in the waters surrounding the Solomon islands. The Allies declared the island secured on February 9, 1943.

A: Ernest King was the Commander-in-Chief of the U.S. Fleet and Chief of Naval Operations, the highest position in the Navy, from March 1942 until November 1945. He was promoted to the rank of Fleet Admiral in 1944.

A: The *kamikazes* ("divine wind" in Japanese) were Japanese suicide squadrons that were created during the last few months of WWII by the Japanese Air Force. These pilots flew their explosive-laden aircraft directly into U.S. naval vessels. They believed they had sacrificed their lives to stop the American forces. The *kamikaze* pilots sank an estimated forty U.S. ships.

A: On October 25, 1944, a *kamikaze* flew into the deck of the carrier Midway (subsequently named St. Lo), causing it to explode and sink.

A: The *shinyo* were the Japanese suicide speedboats. Each carried a single helmsman along with two tons of TNT, and traveled at a speed of 30 knots. The charge exploded upon impact.

Q: What was Hitler's "final solution"?

Q: What was the Wannsee Conference?

Q: How was euthanasia reinterpreted by the Nazis?

Q: What role did Chiang Kai-shek play in the Second World War?

Q: What item did Japanese officers carry that made them recognized as such?

Q: What was Operation Husky?

Q: What George M. Cohan song, written and sung during WWI, was also sung by soldiers during WWII?

A: Hitler, in 1941, decided on his "final solution" (*Endloesung*) to the "Jewish question" in Europe—the extermination of all the Jews.

A: The Wannsee Conference was a Nazi conference convened solely for the purpose of discussing Hitler's "final solution of the Jewish question." The conference was held at Wannsee, Germany on January 20, 1942. All attendants agreed with Hitler's conclusion.

A: Euthanasia is the painless, merciful death of those suffering unbearable pain and incurable sicknesses. In 1939, Hitler decreed the death of those who were considered to be "incurably ill." By the end of August 1941 over 70,000 mentally ill people were murdered because of Hitler's perversion of euthanasia.

A: Chiang Kai-shek of the Chinese Kuomintang Party was the political and military head of China, fighting the Japanese from 1937–1945.

A: During WWII all Japanese officers carried a sword at their side.

A: The Allied invasion of Sicily, which began on July 10, 1943. The Allies moved on to invade Italy in September, allowing them to open a front in Italy.

A: "Over There," originally written in 1917.

Q: What famous Hollywood actress cut her hair to save lives?

Q: What U.S. combat soldier of the 3rd Infantry Battalion accumulated 33 decorations and is credited with killing over 240 of the enemy, while capturing and wounding others?

Q: What did Henry Fonda, Walter Mathau, David Niven, and James Stewart have in common?

Q: What do John Wayne, Frank Sinatra, Errol Flynn, and Gary Cooper have in common?

A: Veronica Lake. Female factory workers, engaged in the war effort, often got their hair caught in the machinery, resulting in injuries or death. Lake cut her world famous locks during WWII to help popularize a new, shorter hairstyle for women.

A: Audie Leon Murphy was the most decorated soldier to come out of WWII, having been awarded 33 decorations, including the Medal of Honor. He also received five decorations from France and Belgium. He was wounded three times, and fought in nine major campaigns in Europe. Audie Murphy is considered to be one of the best combat soldiers ever to have lived.

A: They were all silver screen stars who were decorated in WWII. Henry Fonda was awarded the Bronze Star in the Pacific; Walter Mathau was awarded six Battle Stars while serving on the B-17; David Niven, who fought with the British, was awarded the U.S. Legion of Merit; James Stewart was awarded the Distinguished Flying Cross.

A: They were turned down from serving in WWII because of health reasons. However, all of them supported the war cause in other ways.

Q: What about Clark Gable, Kirk Douglas, Rex Harrison, Mel Brooks, and Ed McMahon?

Q: What role did Rita Hayworth, Betty Grable, and Jean Harlow have in the Second World War?

Q: What British-born stage and screen actor was killed on a passenger plane that fell into the Bay of Biscay?

Q: What American entertainer living in France served as a spy for the French Resistance?

Q: What future U.S. president, when asked about becoming a hero, said "It was involuntary. They sank my boat"?

Q: What WWII general was famous for wearing ivory pistols at his side?

A: They were all stars who left Hollywood to fight for the U.S. Clark Gable worked as a photographer; Kirk Douglas was a Communications Officer; Rex Harrison was a radar operator for the British; Mel Brooks was a combat engineer; Ed McMahon was a Marine Fighter Pilot.

A: They were the most popular pinup girls of WWII.

A: Leslie Howard, an actor best known for his role as the indecisive Ashley Wilkes in the film *Gone With The Wind*, was killed by German fighter planes on June 1, 1943.

A: Josephine Baker, the famous African-American dancer and singer, who starred in movies such as *Zou Zou* and *La Revue Negre*, participated in the French liberation movement.

A: John F. Kennedy, referring to the sinking of his PT boat— PT 109—when struck by a Japanese destroyer.

A: General George Patton.

Q: How many Japanese soldiers died during their invasion and capture of Guam on December 8, 1941?

Q: What was the Bataan Death March?

Q: Who was the Desert Fox?

Q: What was the significance of the battle at El Alamein, Egypt (October 23–November 4, 1942)?

Q: What was the OSS?

Q: Who met at the Tehran Conference in 1943?

A: Only one life was lost on that day.

A: After American soldiers surrendered at Corregidor (northern Philippines) on May 6, 1942, they were executed by the Japanese along with the Filipinos. Those Americans and Filipinos that were not killed were taken on a 65-mile march, during which over 5,000 Americans died.

A: German General Erwin Rommel earned that nickname because of his campaigns in Africa.

A: British General Montgomery decisively defeated German General Rommel. The German loss at El Alamein turned the tide for the Allies in North Africa.

A: The OSS (Office of Strategic Services) was the predecessor of the CIA, and was created on June 13, 1942. Its purpose was to collect information and conduct secret missions behind enemy lines.

A: The Tehran Conference was the first time that the "Big Three" (U.S. President Roosevelt, British Prime Minister Churchill, and Soviet Prime Minister Stalin) met together. The conference was convened in Iran's capital and lasted from November 28 until December 1, 1943.

Q: What agreements were made at the Tehran
   Conference?

Q: What was the Manhattan Project?

Q: Who was the father of the atomic bomb?

Q: What did the word "gadget" mean during
   WWII?

A: The main issue discussed at Tehran was the plan to launch the cross-Channel invasion in 1944 (Operation Overlord, the code name for the final landings at Normandy, France on June 6, 1944). Stalin agreed to launch an offensive attack and to declare war on Japan upon Germany's defeat. Among the many things discussed at the conference was the concept of the United Nations.

A: The Manhattan Project involved the research and development of the atomic bomb. Its name came from the army's code-name for it—the "Manhattan District." The project began in 1939 when two scientists in Berlin successfully accomplished atomic fission. Believing that Germany might successfully develop an atomic bomb, a group of physicists, including Albert Einstein, convinced President Roosevelt to establish a U.S. research program.

A: The man known as the father of the atomic bomb was Robert J. Oppenheimer. Appointed by General Leslie R. Groves as the director of the Los Alamos Scientific Laboratory, Oppenheimer's job was to direct and design the construction of the atomic bombs.

A: While constructing the atomic bomb, Robert Serber, Oppenhiemer's assistant, for security reasons, was told to use the word "gadget" when referring to the bomb.

Q: When did the first testing of the atomic bomb take place?

Q: What were concentration camps?

Q: How did the Nazis identify the different concentration camp populations?

Q: What were some of the more infamous concentration camps in Europe?

Q: How many Jews were killed by the Nazis in the Holocaust? How many non-Jews were also killed?

Q: What was the *Einsatzgruppen*?

Q: When did Italy surrender?

Q: When was Paris, France liberated?

A: The first testing of the atomic bomb took place on July 16, 1945 at Alamogordo, New Mexico.

A: Concentration camps were places in which the Germans placed the people they deemed a danger to their society, like Jews, Gypsies, homosexuals, and political opponents. People were placed in an area with barbed wire surrounding it so that they could not escape; millions of people were exterminated at these camps.

A: They were identified by the different badges or armbands: Jews wore yellow Stars of David; Gypsies wore brown triangles; criminals wore green triangles; Jehovah Witnesses wore yellow triangles; homosexuals wore pink triangles.

A: Theresienstadt, in Bohemia; Auschwitz, Maidanek, and Struttof in Poland; Natzweiler-Struthof in Alsace; Kaunas and Riga in the Baltic States; Neuengamme, Gross-Rosen, Bergen-Belsen, Butchewald, and Dora in Germany.

A: Approximately 6 million Jews were murdered. 6 million non-Jews were also killed.

A: The *Einsatzgruppen* were a group of Nazi killers who followed the Army, rounded up Jews, and executed them.

A: Italy surrendered to the Allied powers on September 8, 1943.

A: The Americans liberated Paris on August 25, 1944.

Q: Where did Germany stage its last counterattack in December 1944?

Q: What land battle of WWII had the greatest number of participants?

Q: What new plan of attack did Hitler launch during the Battle of the Bulge?

Q: What WWII figure's name has become synonymous with being a traitor?

A: The Ardennes is where the Germans staged their last counterattack, at the Battle of the Bulge. The Americans were
taken by surprise, and driven back at the areas of St. Vith
and Bastogne. As the weather cleared, the Allies were able to
use their air superiority to win the battle.

A: The Battle of the Bulge, which started on December 16,
1944 and ended on January 28, 1945. More than one million
men fought in this battle.

A: The Great Blow. The ultimate goal of this plan was to elimi-
nate the superior Allied air power. At 8:00 A.M. on January
1, 1945, German fighter planes flew over Belgium, France,
and Holland and for two consecutive hours bombed the
Allied airfields. A whopping 206 planes lay in ruin. Hitler's
plan damaged the Allied air power deeply, but a high price
was paid for this victory—the *Luftwaffe* lost 300 planes and
253 skilled pilots.

A: Vidkum Quisling, the pro-Hitler Norwegian, and Norway's
most infamous traitor. His name has come to refer to a traitor—he or she is a "Quisling." It was first used by Winston
Churchill. Quisling was executed after WWII.

Q: What military article of clothing was connected to the ad: "Even if he is 4F, he can feel like a hero"?

Q: What Walt Disney film with a WWII background won an Academy Award for the Best Visual Effects?

Q: What comedy starring Cary Grant and released in 1964 had a WWII background?

Q: Which Oscar-winning and knighted English actor portrayed Adolf Hitler on screen?

Q: What is the name of Norman Mailer's novel based on his wartime experiences?

A: "Ike jackets," like the one worn by General Dwight D. Eisenhower. Sold by Lord & Taylor in New York the ad promised that its shoppers could feel like a military hero—in spite of having been rejected by the army for having flat feet, being near sighted, or other various aliments—simply by purchasing an Ike jacket.

A: *Bedknobs and Broomsticks* (1971), starring Angela Lansbury and David Tomilson is a humorous and lighthearted tale about a would-be witch who wants to gain magical powers in order that she help her fellow countrymen defeat the Germans.

A: *Father Goose*, starring Cary Grant, Leslie Caron, and Trevor Howard, was a delightful comedy about a man who is forced by his friend to report sightings of enemy bomber planes on a deserted island. He unexpectedly meets a woman and several children stranded on the island, which is about to be swarmed with Japanese soldiers. In the mist of all the craziness of the war, these two find themselves falling in love.

A: Sir Alec Guinness portrayed Hitler in the 1973 film *Hitler: The Last Ten Days*. (Guinness won an Oscar for best actor for his role in *The Bridge on the River Kwai* (1957) and was knighted by Queen Elizabeth in 1959.)

A: *The Naked and The Dead* (1948).

Q: What famous actress lost her life in a plane crash while on a U.S. bond tour?

Q: What WWII battle was largest amphibious landing in military history?

Q: Who commanded the armies on D-Day?

Q: Who commanded the Allied land forces *after* the landing at Normandy by U.S. soldiers?

A: Carole Lombard died on January 16, 1942 when a plane, in which she and her mother were passengers, crashed into the Table Rock Mountain, which is outside of Las Vegas. Lombard was the wife of Clark Gable.

A: On June 6, 1944, D-Day, the Allied forces invaded the Cotentin Peninsula within Nazi occupied Normandy. This invasion was the largest amphibious landing in military history.

A: The D-Day operation was under the direction of the Supreme Allied Commander Dwight D. Eisenhower. Under his direction was Omar Bradley, commanding the U.S. First Army (which invaded Utah and Omaha beaches); General Maxwell Taylor's 101st Airborne, and General Matthew Ridgway's 82nd Airborne (which landed by parachute and glider behind the German lines); General Bernard Montgomery's 21st Army (British); and General Brian Dempsey's British 2nd Army (which invaded Gold, June and Sword beaches).

A: Upon the completion of the D-Day landings at Normandy (June 6, 1944), the command of all Allied land forces fell to British General Bernard Montgomery, in fulfillment of an agreement that had given Eisenhower supreme command authority once the U.S. entered the war.

Q: What was the fate of the USS *Corry*?

Q: What does the "D" in D-Day stand for?

Q: Who said: "Give me an army of West Point grads and I'll win a battle; give me a handful of Texas Aggies and I'll win a war"?

Q: In 1945, what important cargo was the U.S. Cruiser *Indianapolis* carrying when it crossed from California to the Marianas in the South Pacific where the U.S. had its B-29 air base?

Q: Who was the German businessman, who at the risk of his own life, saved over one thousand Jews during WWII?

A: German gunfire sank the destroyer the USS *Corry* on D-Day, June 6, 1944.

A: The "D" in D-Day stands for day—an abbreviation of Day plus Day.

A: General Patton.

A: The *Indianapolis* was ferrying the atomic bomb that would be dropped on Hiroshima. On July 30, 1945, just four days after delivering the bomb components, the *Indianapolis* was sunk in the Pacific by a Japanese submarine; with a loss of more than 800 men, it was the greatest loss of life in U.S. Naval history.

A: Oskar Schindler risked his life to save the Jews working for him. He used bribery, black marketing, and lies to keep the Jews working at his *Emalia* factory and kept them from the Germans "final solution."

Q: What do Pee Wee Reese (Brooklyn Dodgers shortstop), Yogi Berra (New York Yankee catcher), Hank Greenberg (Detroit Tigers first baseman), Bob Feller (Cleveland Indians pitcher), Joe DiMaggio (New York Yankee out-fielder), and Ted Williams (Boston Red Sox outfielder) have in common?

Q: What bestseller that came out of World War II was made into a serious Broadway play?

Q: What Pulitzer Prize winning book, whose sub-ject concerned WWII, was fashioned into a Broadway musical that won a Tony Award?

Q: What was the disparaging phrase often applied to the women who married U.S. service men bound to war for their monthly checks?

A: These patriotic baseball heroes all enlisted in the U.S. forces during WWII.

A: *The Diary of Anne Frank.* The play opened in New York City at the Broadway Cort Theatre on October 5, 1955, with actress Susan Strasberg portraying Anne Frank. Based on *Anne Frank: The Diary of A Young Girl*, which was first published in Holland in 1947, it was the diary of 16-year-old Anne Frank, who was killed in March, 1945 at Bergen-Belsen, a German concentration camp. The play was adapted by Francis Goodrich and Albert Hackett from Frank's diary. The play won a Pulitzer Prize for Drama and a Tony Award for Best Play.

A: The musical was *South Pacific,* based on James Michener's *Tales of the South Pacific* (1947). It opened on Broadway at the Majestic Theatre April 7, 1949; Mary Martin and Ezio Pinza were in the lead parts, with music by Richard Rodgers, book and lyrics by Oscar Hammerstein II. The book won a Pulitzer Prize and the play won the Tony Award for Best Musical.

A: "Allotment Annies" was the name applied to these women who married GIs for no other reason than their monthly $50 allowance. Also, an Allotment Annie could cash in the standard government issue $10,000 life insurance policy should the husbands not make it back. Some of these gold diggers were married to several GIs at the same time.

Q: Who said: "Books cannot be killed by fire.
People die, but books never die. No man and no
force can abolish memory... In this war, we
know, books are weapons"?

Q: What remains little known about the Pulitzer
Prize winning photograph of the Marines raising the American flag on Iwo Jima, on February
23, 1945?

Q: What did Switzerland agree to on February 6,
2001 regarding something that happened during WWII?

Q: Can you name the famous Third Reich cabinet
minister who has the distinction of being the
last prisoner held in the Tower of London?

A: On April 23, 1942, President Franklin Roosevelt said this to the American Booksellers Association in reference to the Nazi book burning of 1933.

A: The photograph was staged. Earlier that day the flag had been raised, but was taken down and raised a second time to accommodate Joe Rosenthal who photographed the raising of the Stars and Stripes. The photograph appeared in the military newspaper *Stars & Stripes* before being run in other newspapers and won Rosenthal a Pulitzer Prize.

A: The Swiss government, under world pressure, agreed to post on the Internet and publicize the names of some 21,000 Holocaust survivors whose money had been laying dormant in Swiss banks for more than fifty years.

A: Rudolf Hess, who on May 10, 1941, fled Germany aboard an ME-110 and parachuted into Scotland. Arrested by the Brits, who did not buy his tale that he was on a peace mission, Hess was imprisoned in the same Tower of London that once held Saint Thomas Moore and Mary Queen of Scots. Hess remained there until the Nuremberg Trials, where he was sentenced to Germany's Spandau prison.

Q: What was the significance of the Yalta Conference and when did it take place?

Q: The bombing of what German city, crowded with war refugees, turned the city to ashes?

Q: What was Charlemagne?

Q: What was ODESSA?

Q: In their pursuit of the German armies in March 1945, at what bridge were the Allies first able to cross the Rhine?

A: The Yalta Conference took place from February 4–12, 1945 at Yalta, Ukraine. During the conference, Churchill (Great Britain), Roosevelt (U.S.), and Stalin (the Soviet Union)—known as "the Big Three"—agreed to require the unconditional surrender of Germany. Upon this surrender, a four power occupation of Germany would take place, France being the fourth power. This conference also stipulated a founding conference of the United Nations. The Soviets also agreed to join the fight with Japan after the fall of Germany.

A: Dresden. Considered the most beautiful city in all of Germany, it had absolutely no military significance. Yet on February 13–15, 1945, more than 1,200 Allied bombers obliterated the city. The destruction of Dresden was morally unjustified, and it has never been clear why it was bombed.

A: Charlemagne was a division of the French SS that was founded in October 1944. The members of Charlemagne fought on the Russian front in February 1944, and in the Baltic in March 1945. Then, in a last-ditch battle, they fought to save Hitler's bunker in April 1945.

A: ODESSA (*Organisation der SS Angehoerigen*, or Organization of SS Members) was the secret network created to arrange the escape of several SS members prosecuted at the Nuremberg Trials.

A: The 9th Armored Division of the U.S. First Army reached the Remagen Railway Bridge (near Bonn) before the Germans were able to destroy it; they established the first Allied bridgehead across the Rhine.

Q: What did Adolf Hitler do on the day before his death, April 29, 1945, that he had never done before?

Q: Who died along with Adolf Hitler and Eva Braun, his wife of one day, in their suicide pact?

Q: What was Adolf Hitler's last meal?

Q: Did Hitler's will name a successor?

Q: When did Germany surrender to the Allied powers?

Q: What was the Potsdam Conference, and when did it take place?

A: Hitler acceded to the wishes of his sweetheart Eva Braun and married in a civil ceremony in a bunker under Berlin's chancellery.

A: On April 30, 1945 Hitler's Alsatian dog Blondie was also killed, to prevent Blondie from falling into the hands of the Allies.

A: On April 30, 1945, Hitler and Eva Braun ate spaghetti marinara and a salad.

A: Yes, Karl Dönitz, who became Germany's last Führer. It was Dönitz who presided over the unconditional surrender of Germany; he was tried and sentenced to 10 years in prison at the Nuremberg Trials.

A: On May 7, 1945, Germany surrendered unconditionally.

A: The Potsdam Conference (Potsdam, Germany), the last of the major conferences, was held from July 17 until August 2, 1945, after the Third Reich had fallen. Attending the conference was Soviet Prime Minister Joseph Stalin, English Prime Minister Winston Churchill (he was replaced on July 28 by his successor Clement Atlee) and the new American President, Harry S. Truman.

Q: What agreements and events took place during the Potsdam Conference?

Q: When did the Soviet Union declare war on Japan?

Q: When were the Japanese cities Hiroshima and Nagasaki bombed by the atomic bomb?

Q: Why did President Truman decide to use the atomic bomb on Japan?

Q: What planes were responsible for dropping the atomic bomb on Hiroshima and Nagasaki?

Q: What were the nicknames the Americans gave the bombs that were dropped on Hiroshima and Nagasaki?

A: During the Potsdam Conference, President Truman informed Prime Minister Churchill of the success of the Manhattan Project; America had a working and fully operational atomic bomb. Prime Minister Stalin was informed that America had a "new weapon." The three powerful leaders decided to demand the unconditional surrender of Japan.

A: August 8, 1945.

A: The atomic bomb was dropped on Hiroshima on August 6, 1945 by the Americans; three days later, on August 9, 1945, Nagasaki was bombed also.

A: President Truman decided to deploy the atomic bomb because he felt that too many American lives would be lost if he attacked Japan with conventional forces.

A: B-29 Super Fortresses; the *Enola Gay* (Hiroshima) and *Bock's Car* (Nagasaki).

A: The bomb dropped on Hiroshima was nicknamed "Little Boy," and the bomb dropped on Nagasaki was nicknamed "Fat Man."

Q: What bomb carried the message "Greetings to the Emperor from the men of the *Indianapolis*"?

Q: Who was Colonel Paul W. Tibbet?

Q: Who piloted the B-29 Super Fortress *Bock's Car*?

Q: Who were the shadow people?

Q: When did V-E Day take place?

Q: When did V-J Day take place?

A: "Little Boy" was the bomb that carried this message and was dropped from the *Enola Gay* on Hiroshima, Japan.

A: Colonel Paul W. Tibbet was the man chosen to deliver the "package" to Hiroshima. He piloted the B-29 Super Fortress *Enola Gay*, named after his mother. On August 6, 1945 he dropped Little Boy on Hiroshima, the first atomic bomb ever used in war. Little Boy exploded 1,300 feet over Hiroshima, with a force equal to some 14,300 tons of TNT. About 130,000 people were killed instantly that day.

A: Major Charles W. Sweeney. On August 9, 1945, three days after the bombing of Hiroshima, he dropped Fat Man on Nagasaki. Fat Man exploded with the force of 10 kilotons, destroyed almost two square miles of the city, and killed, instantly, 45,000 people.

A: The shadow people were the ashy remains of the people who were instantly incinerated by the atomic bomb. All that was left of these people were their footprints, or their dark, ashy imprints on walls or buildings, that resembled shadows.

A: V-E day, which stood for victory in Europe, took place on May 8, 1945.

A: V-J Day, victory over Japan day, took place on August 15, 1945.

Q: What historic event occurred on August 14, 1945?

Q: When did WWII officially end?

Q: How many people died in WWII?

Q: Which nation lost 136 of its generals during WWII?

Q: What Allied power country suffered the most casualties and deaths during WWII?

Q: What were the Nuremberg Trials?

A: The Japanese nation surrendered to the Allied powers on August 14, 1945, five days after the bombing of Nagasaki. On September 2, 1945, on board the USS *Missouri,* they went through the formalities of signing official papers declaring their surrender. The Second World War was over.

A: WWII officially ended the day the Japanese signed the surrender agreement on September 2, 1945.

A: More than 56 million people were killed during the war, with civilians making up over one-half of this number.

A: The German Army—an exceedingly high loss.

A: During World War II the Soviet Union suffered the most casualties of war. An estimated eleven million of their military died, and over seven million of their civilians were killed.

A: Before a board of select judges from the Allied countries, the Nuremberg trials began on November 20, 1945. The International Military Tribunal tried high-ranking Nazi officials for their actions in WWII that contravened the laws of war and against humanity. Among the charges were plotting and waging an aggressive war, abusing and murdering innocent people and war prisoners.

Q: Which high-ranking Nazis were sentenced to death at the Nuremberg Trials?

Q: Were the men tried at Nuremberg the only ones tried for war crimes in Europe?

A: Twelve death sentences were given: Martin Bormann, tried *in absentia*, (Deputy Führer) who was believed dead; Hermann Goering (*Reichsmarschall*, Chief of Air Force) committed suicide on October 15, 1946 the night before his scheduled execution; Joachim von Ribbentrop (Minister of Foreign Affairs), Ernst Kaltenbrunner (Chief of Reich Main Security including the SS and Gestapo), Wihelm Frick (Minister of the Interior), Hans Frank (Governor-General of Occupied Poland), Fritz Sauckel (Labor Leader), Julius Streicher (Director of the Central Committee of the Defense against the "Jewish Atrocity"), Wilhelm Keitel (Chief of Staff of High Command of the Armed Forces), Alfred Jodl (Chief of Army Operations), Arthur Seyss-Inquart (Commisar of Netherlands), and Alfred Rosenberg (Minister of the Occupied Eastern Territories) were all hanged. One of the twenty-four men accused committed suicide before the trial began, one man was considered "too frail" to try, three men were sentenced to life in prison, and four men were acquitted.

A: The American, British, and French courts, from 1947 until 1953, tried 10,400 people, sentenced 5,025 people to prison terms, and executed 806 prisoners. The officials from the German Democratic Republic brought about 12,821 war criminals to trial.

Q: Who was the Nazi leader who was found in Argentina many years after the war and was brought to trial and hanged?

Q: What were the Tokyo Trials?

Q: Were any of the major war criminals at the Tokyo Trials found guilty?

Q: Were these major war criminals tried at the Tokyo Trials the only ones convicted?

A: Adolf Eichmann was charged for his participation in "the final solution." Eichmann was found and kidnapped in May 1960 near Buenos Aires by Israeli agents and brought to Israel to stand trial. He was judged and sentenced to death on December 15, 1961. He was hanged on June 1, 1962.

A: The Tokyo Tials were the Nuremberg Trials of the East. The International Military Tribunal was set up in Tokyo in May, 1946 to try Japanese war criminals. About 26 people were indicted; two men died during the trials.

A: Yes, all of the major Japanese leaders were found guilty. The sentence was death by hanging for Prime Minister Hideki Tojo, Foreign Minister Koki Hirota and five generals (Kenji Doihara, Seishiro Itagaki, Hyoturo Kimura, Iwane Matsui and Akira Muto). Sixteen others got life in prison. Two were given prison time.

A: No—it is estimated that 5,600 Japanese were tried for war crimes. Out of the 5,600 tried 4,400 were convicted and 1,000 were executed for their crimes.